CW00672670

SOCCER

Interactive Quiz

Managing Editors: Simon Melhuish and Sarah Wells
Series Editor: Nikole G Bamford
Designer: Linley J Clode
Writer: Lee Linford
Illustrator: Gary Sherwood

Published by
The Lagoon Group
PO Box 311, KT2 5QW, UK
PO Box 990676, Boston, MA 02199, USA

ISBN: 1904797148

www.thelagoongroup.com

Printed in China

SOCCER

Interactive Quiz

IntelliQuest

UNIQUE BOOK CODE	004

Instructions

First of all make sure you have a Quizmo —

Find the book's unique code (this appears at the top of this page). Use the < and > buttons to scroll to this number on the Quizmo screen. Press the ⬥ button to enter the code, and you're ready to go.

Use the < > scroll buttons to select the question number you want to answer. Press the A, B, C, or D button to enter your chosen answer.

If you are correct the green light beside the button you pressed will flash. You can then use the scroll button to move on to another question.

If your answer is incorrect, the red light beside the button you pressed will flash.

Don't worry, you can try again and again until you have
the correct answer, OR move on to another question.
(Beware: the more times you guess incorrectly, the lower
your final percentage score will be!)

You can finish the quiz at any point — just press
the ⬥ button to find out your score and rank as follows:

75% or above	A champion score!
50% — 74%	A top-flight performance!
25% — 49%	Have you thought of taking up golf?
Less than 25%	Red card! Off!

If you do press the ⬥ button to find out your score,
this will end your session and you will have to use
the ⬥ to start again!

HAVE FUN!

001

Which two teams kicked off the 2002 World Cup finals?

A France and Uruguay

B Uruguay and Denmark

C France and Senegal

D Republic of Ireland and Cameroon

002

Which is the only country to have taken part in every World Cup tournament to date?

A Uruguay

B Brazil

C Argentina

D Romania

003

At what stage did Germany bow out of the 1998 World Cup finals?

A Second phase

B First round

C Semi-finals

D Quarter-finals

Italy have won the World Cup in each of the following countries, with the exception of one. Which is it?

`004`

- **A** Italy
- **B** France
- **C** Sweden
- **D** Spain

What was the estimated cumulative television audience across the globe for the 1998 World Cup finals?

`005`

- **A** 10 billion
- **B** 25 billion
- **C** 35 billion
- **D** 50 billion

Iordan Letchkov played for which national side during the 1994 World Cup?

`006`

- **A** Poland
- **B** Bulgaria
- **C** Hungary
- **D** Russia

007

Who blasted a blistering Brazilian fourth past the Italian keeper in the 1970 World Cup Final?

A Pelé
B Gerson
C Jairzinho
D Carlos Alberto

008

Which Brazilian star dropped in the perfect pass that resulted in this goal?

A Pelé
B Gerson
C Jairzinho
D Carlos Alberto

009

In the 1974 World Cup finals, which underdog footballing nation astonished Italy by taking the lead in a first round match?

A Iran
B Zaire
C Haiti
D El Salvador

010

The 2010 World Cup is set to be staged on the soil of which continent?

- **A** Asia
- **B** Africa
- **C** Europe
- **D** South America

011

Which of the following South American teams has never succeeded in reaching the World Cup finals?

- **A** Chile
- **B** Peru
- **C** Bolivia
- **D** Ecuador

012

The draw for the 1994 World Cup qualifiers was held in the host country for the first time ever. Where did the draw take place?

- **A** Los Angeles
- **B** Washington DC
- **C** Chicago
- **D** New York

013

Who was the top goalscorer of the 1958 World Cup?

- **A** Just Fontaine (France)
- **B** Helmut Rahn (West Germany)
- **C** Vava (Brazil)
- **D** Pelé (Brazil)

014

Where was the 10th World Cup tournament held?

- **A** Mexico
- **B** West Germany
- **C** Chile
- **D** Argentina

015

Why did Cameroon's football squad turn up three days later than planned for the 2002 World Cup?

- **A** Their passports were mislaid by the team coach and the team was stranded in Paris until new ones could be issued
- **B** Their flight tickets were incorrectly booked and the team ended up in Jamaica
- **C** They went on strike at Charles de Gaulle airport, whilst en-route to the tournament
- **D** Several of the players went AWOL after a drunken night out in Paris

016

In which year did Diego Maradona's infamous 'hand of god' prevent England from progressing to the World Cup semi-finals?

A 1990
B 1986
C 1982
D 1978

017

When did England first participate in a World Cup tournament?

A 1954
B 1950
C 1946
D 1942

018

Why was this the first time they took part?

A They had previously declined to become members of FIFA
B The costs associated with entering the tournament had been considered frivolous
C They failed to qualify for previous tournaments
D Clubs had previously refused to release players for the national team during the tournament's infancy

019

With which country did El Salvador go to war as a direct result of their tempestuous World Cup qualifying matches in 1970?

A Guatemala

B Nicaragua

C Honduras

D Mexico

020

How did Spain's goalkeeper, Santiago Canizares, sustain an injury that kept him from playing in the 2002 World Cup?

A He was thrown from an out-of-control golf buggy

B He karate-kicked a burglar

C He tripped over his bootlaces

D He dropped a bottle of aftershave on his foot

021

Which of the following nations did Iraq not have to face during their short-lived World Cup finals debut in 1986?

A Belgium

B Paraguay

C Italy

D Mexico

Why did the USA trainer have to be carried off unconscious during a 1930 World Cup match against Argentina?

022

A He was too excited

B He had been hit by the ball

C He had broken a bottle of chloroform

D He had been punched by an Argentinian player

Why was Gazza reduced to tears in the semi-final of the Italia 1990 World Cup?

023

A He was kicked in the groin

B He was shown a red card, meaning a match suspension should England have progressed to the final

C He missed his shot during the deciding penalty shootout

D He was shown a yellow card, meaning a match suspension should England have progressed to the final

In which year did Spain host the World Cup finals?

024

A 1970

B 1982

C 1978

D 1974

025

During the 2002 World Cup, Steve Staunton became the first Irish player to do what?

A Earn his 100th cap

B Captain his team to a draw with Germany

C Win the FIFA Fair Play Award

D Score a golden goal for Ireland

026

Which of these teams were NOT drawn in the same group as England for the 2002 World Cup?

A Denmark

B Argentina

C Nigeria

D Sweden

027

Who were the losing side in both the 1934 and 1962 World Cup Finals?

A Chile

B Brazil

C Italy

D Czechoslovakia

028

When France failed to qualify for the 1994 World Cup tournament, what did Gerard Houllier brand David Ginola?

A A criminal
B A disgrace
C An imbecile
D An idiot

029

Having opposed the idea of staging a World Championship for football, which country subsequently put forward a bid to host the inaugural tournament?

A Holland
B Hungary
C Uruguay
D Sweden

030

What was the nationality of Japan's 2002 World Cup coach?

A French
B Swedish
C Russian
D Dutch

031

The second half of the 1930 World Cup group clash between Argentina and France was delayed for what reason?

A The referee lost his whistle

B There was a pitch invasion prompted by the referee blowing the half-time whistle prematurely

C The match balls were stolen

D A dressing room fight between French players had to be broken up

032

King Carol of Romania took what unusual step when his nation embarked upon their World Cup quest in 1930?

A He financed the team's expenses using royal funds

B He personally selected the players

C He appointed royal tailors to hand-stitch the team kit

D He dyed his hair blonde and decreed that every member of the team should do the same

033

Which country knocked Brazil out of the 1930 World Cup tournament?

A Bolivia

B Mexico

C USA

D Yugoslavia

Which of these teams was not seeded for the 1930 World Cup tournament?

034

- **A** Argentina
- **B** Uruguay
- **C** Paraguay
- **D** USA

Why was Uruguyan goalkeeper, Mazáli, dropped from the nation's 1930 World Cup squad?

035

- **A** The player refused to cut his hair at the request of the national manager
- **B** FIFA challenged the player's nationality and lacked necessary documentation to dispute their challenge
- **C** He ignored a curfew imposed on the players during their preparation for the tournament
- **D** He was arrested for brawling with one of the team's coaches in a hotel foyer

Which of the following statements about the 1930 World Cup tournament is untrue?

036

- **A** There were no qualifying matches
- **B** Thirteen teams participated
- **C** There were six groups
- **D** Italy, Spain, Holland and Sweden pulled out prior to the start of the tournament

037 What were the USA squad dubbed in the 1930 World Cup tournament?

A The Body Builders

B The Tanks

C The Bulldozers

D The Shot Putters

038 What did Uruguay offer to improve their chances of staging the inaugural World Cup tournament?

A To make a sizeable donation to FIFA

B To pay for the casting of the tournament trophy

C To negotiate with their South American neighbors to ensure a minimum of four participant nations from the continent

D To pay the traveling costs for all participating nations

039 How many stadiums were used to stage the 1930 World Cup?

A Three

B One

C Five

D Eight

Who is known as the 'Father of Football'?

040

- **A** Ebeneezer Cobb Morley
- **B** Charles W. Alcock
- **C** Alf Ramsey
- **D** William McGregor

In which year was the Football Association formed?

041

- **A** 1858
- **B** 1868
- **C** 1863
- **D** 1873

Which English club is recognized as the world's oldest league football club?

042

- **A** Notts County
- **B** Aston Villa
- **C** Nottingham Forest
- **D** Derby County

043

In the early days, why were some players given a florin (coin) to hold in each hand?

A To prevent them from handling the ball upon the introduction of ball-handling restrictions

B To dissuade them from pushing opponents off the ball and conceding a free kick

C As a match bonus for important games; the coins could be kept if the match was won

D As a lucky charm

044

The medieval game of Shrovetide football may be considered distasteful today for what reason?

A The losing team could expect to receive a flogging

B The ball was usually a hog's head or an inflated sheep's bladder

C It was not uncommon for lynch mobs to pursue the referee

D Crowd trouble could result in the burning of villages

045

'Money' was the term used for what?

A A player's signing-on fee

B A set allowance provided by clubs for players to spend on their boots

C Financial inducements left in a player's boot

D A token sum of money presented to the first goalscorer in a match

The earliest forms of football have been traced back to around the 2nd Century B.C. In which country was evidence of this discovered?

046

A Japan
B China
C Italy
D Greece

How many players participated in a game of Shrovetide football?

047

A 22
B 50
C An unlimited number
D 107

Why did Edward III, Richard II, Henry IV and Henry V all forbid the playing of football?

048

A They believed that any such free time should be used for educational pursuits
B They believed that time would be better spent honing military skills such as archery
C They were concerned that the game would generate powerful figures, potentially of threat to the monarchy
D They wanted open common land to be used only for equestrian events

049

J. Mitchell, goalkeeper for Preston in the twenties, is the only player recorded as having worn what during an FA Cup final?

A A hearing aid

B Glasses

C A neck brace

D A leg cast

050

How did Aston Villa prevent Stoke from taking a penalty during a match in the 1892-93 season?

A The Villa captain kicked the ball out of the grounds and by the time it had been found, the final whistle had blown

B The entire Aston Villa team sat around the penalty spot and refused to move

C Villa's captain burst the only ball they had

D While the players and referee argued, Villa's manager ran onto the pitch with a spade and mutilated the penalty spot

What was the European Championship titled until 1968? `051`

- **A** The European Continental Cup
- **B** The UEFA Nations' Cup
- **C** The European Nations' Cup
- **D** The European Associations Cup

Where were the first European Championship finals held? `052`

- **A** Italy
- **B** USSR
- **C** France
- **D** Spain

How did Germany win the 1996 European Championship Final? `053`

- **A** They scored a Golden Goal
- **B** They won on penalties
- **C** The Czech Republic scored an own goal in the final minute
- **D** Their captain completed a hat-trick in the final minute of the game

054

Why were Azerbaijan forced to play their 1996 European Championship home games in Turkey?

A Due to civil war

B They didn't have a suitable stadium in which to conduct the matches

C Several nations refused to send their national squads to Azerbaijan

D The Azerbaijan government refused to issue sufficient visas for visiting players

055

Which of the following countries were not in the same group as England at Euro 2004?

A Macedonia

B Liechenstein

C Estonia

D Slovakia

056

Which two teams competed in the first European Championship Final to be decided by a penalty shoot-out?

A West Germany and Czechoslovakia

B Czechoslovakia and Belgium

C Belgium and West Germany

D Italy and the Soviet Union

The European Championship trophy is called what?

`057`

A The Henri Delaunay Trophy

B The Ernst Thommen Trophy

C The Ottorino Barrasi Trophy

D The Robert Guérin Trophy

When did Holland finally succeed in taking the European Championship title?

`058`

A 1974

B 1978

C 1984

D 1988

Which Soviet star secured the 1960 European Championship for the USSR by scoring in the last seven minutes of the Final?

`059`

A Oleg Makarov

B Oleg Blokhin

C Viktor Ponedelnik

D Mikhail Meskhi

060

Which four nations reached the European Championship semi-finals in 1984?

- **A** Germany, Spain, Belgium & Denmark
- **B** Denmark, Portugal, Romania & France
- **C** France, Denmark, Portugal & Spain
- **D** Spain, Holland, France & Germany

– The FA Cup –

In which year was the FA Cup established? `061`

- **A** 1862
- **B** 1863
- **C** 1868
- **D** 1871

Who won the 2002 FA Cup Final? `062`

- **A** Chelsea
- **B** Arsenal
- **C** Manchester United
- **D** Liverpool

Why was the 1923 FA Cup Final of particular significance? `063`

- **A** It was played at Wembley for the first time
- **B** It was won by an amateur team for the first time
- **C** The final score set the record of the highest ever in an FA Cup Final
- **D** It was the first FA Cup final to be decided on penalties

064

Which team won the FA Cup Final for three consecutive years: 1884, 1885 and 1886?

A Aston Villa

B Preston North End

C Old Etonians

D Blackburn Rovers

065

Who was the first player in the 20th century to win four FA Cup Winners' medals?

A Mark Hughes

B Bobby Charlton

C Gary Lineker

D Stanley Matthews

066

What happened during the FA Cup Final in both 1946 and 1947?

A The ball burst

B The match was abandoned due to extreme weather conditions

C The referee had to be replaced

D Captains on both sides were sent off

Which two teams contested the 1933 FA Cup Final?

067

- **A** Manchester United and Manchester City
- **B** Everton and Coventry City
- **C** Manchester City and Everton
- **D** Coventry City and Birmingham City

In 1991, to whom was Terry Venables referring when he declared that he had witnessed "the best free-kick in the history of the FA Cup"?

068

- **A** Alan Shearer
- **B** Paul Gascoigne
- **C** David Platt
- **D** Niall Quinn

Which Manchester City goalkeeper played the last 15 minutes of the 1956 FA Cup final with a broken neck and claimed that season's Footballer of the Year award plus a winner's medal?

069

- **A** Bert Trautmann
- **B** Peter Kippax
- **C** Harry Dowd
- **D** Joe Corrigan

070

In which of the following years did Arsenal fail to win the First Division Championship?

A 1931
B 1932
C 1933
D 1934

071

Who were the first commercial sponsors of the Football League?

A Barclays Bank
B Canon
C Littlewoods
D Carling

072

The one millionth Football League game was played between which two clubs?

A Chelsea and Blackburn Rovers
B Ipswich Town and Oxford United
C Port Vale and Burnley
D Hartlepool United and Brentford

Who chipped a ball over Bruce Grobbelaar's head in the fading moments of injury time to ensure that Arsenal snatched the 1989 Football League championship from the hands of Liverpool?

073

- **A** Lee Dixon
- **B** Alan Smith
- **C** Paul Merson
- **D** Michael Thomas

How many goals did Aston Villa put between the posts during the 1930-31 football season, setting the Division 1 record for the most goals scored in a season?

074

- **A** 128
- **B** 138
- **C** 118
- **D** 148

Why was the 1929-30 season particularly memorable for Brentford?

075

- **A** They didn't lose a single game
- **B** They didn't lose a single away game
- **C** They didn't lose a single home game
- **D** It was the year the club was established

076

How many League championships did Arsenal win during Herbert Chapman's nine-year management of the club?

- **A** 4
- **B** 5
- **C** 7
- **D** 9

077

Manchester United, holders of the unflattering record of most consecutive Division 1 league defeats in a season, lost how many games at the beginning of the 1930-31 season before they managed to break their miserable run?

- **A** 9
- **B** 12
- **C** 15
- **D** 18

078

What did the League Cup become in 1986?

- **A** The Milk Cup
- **B** The Coca-Cola Cup
- **C** The Littlewoods Cup
- **D** The Rumbelows Cup

How many players from England's domestic league participated in the 2002 World Cup tournament?

079

- **A** 78
- **B** 152
- **C** 101
- **D** 212

When an already relegated Leicester Fosse lost 12-0 to Nottingham Forest in 1909 – handing promotion to Forest at the same time – what did official investigations into their dubious performance reveal?

080

- **A** None of Leicester Fosse's regular players had played; instead the team had been cobbled together by the manager, comprising his friends and family members
- **B** The players had gone to the game directly from an all-night poker session
- **C** The club had been unable to afford transportation to the game and the players had cycled from Leicester to Nottingham to participate
- **D** The players had overindulged at a wedding celebration the day before the game had taken place

081 When was the Charity Shield competition established?

A 1900

B 1908

C 1916

D 1924

082 What unusual occurrence featured in the 1967 Charity Shield game?

A The game went to penalties, but not a single goal was scored until 'sudden death'

B The referee scored

C A linesman was dismissed

D Goalkeeper, Pat Jennings, scored

083 The FA Charity Shield became what in 2002?

A The FA Charity Cup

B The FA Charity Trophy

C The FA Community Shield

D The FA Community Cup

In which year was it decided to stage the Charity Shield at Wembley Stadium?

- **A** 1980
- **B** 1976
- **C** 1978
- **D** 1974

085

In 2002, who won the European Super Cup for the first time in the history of the competition?

- **A** Real Madrid
- **B** Feyenoord
- **C** Bayer Leverkusen
- **D** Leeds

086

Which of these players failed to score for Liverpool in the European Super Cup Final, 2001?

- **A** Emil Heskey
- **B** Robbie Fowler
- **C** Michael Owen
- **D** John Arne Riise

087

The Super Cup was originally the brainwave of which Dutch newspaper?

- **A** De Telegraaf
- **B** De Times
- **C** Algemeen Dagblad
- **D** De Volkskrant

When did UEFA officially recognize the European Super Cup as a competitive event?

- **A** 1971
- **B** 1972
- **C** 1973
- **D** 1974

089 Who won the European Champions Cup, 1985-6?

- **A** PSV Eindhoven
- **B** FC Porto
- **C** Steaua Bucharest
- **D** Red Star Belgrade

090 Who beat Manchester United in the semi-finals of the 1957 European Cup?

- **A** PSV Eindhoven
- **B** Benfica
- **C** Milan
- **D** Real Madrid

091 The first European Cup Final to be decided in extra time was played in which year?

- **A** 1953
- **B** 1958
- **C** 1963
- **D** 1968

Why were Marseille unable to defend their 1993 European Cup title in 1994?

`092`

A They pulled out of the competition to allow their players to train with the national squad for the World Cup

B The club was declared bankrupt between the two competitions

C They were banned for match-fixing

D The clubs' players were on strike

Who scored the winning goal in injury time during the 1999 European Cup final, ensuring a 'Treble' win for Manchester United?

`093`

A David Beckham

B Teddy Sheringham

C Jesper Blomqvist

D Ole Gunnar Solskjaer

Which European city became the scene of jubilant partying by Celtic fans upon the club's victory in the European Cup Final, 1967?

`094`

A Madrid

B Turin

C Lisbon

D Stockholm

095

Which club fielded the first English European Cup-winning side?

A West Ham United

B Manchester United

C Liverpool

D Tottenham Hotspur

096

Between its inception in 1960 and its abolition, which club participated in the European Cup Winners' Cup a total of fourteen times?

A Glentoran

B Chelsea

C Cardiff City

D Rangers

097

In which year was the last ever European Cup Winners' Cup Final held?

A 1998

B 1999

C 2000

D 2001

098

Who took the title for the very last time?

A Real Mallorca

B Olympique Marseille

C VFB Stuttgart

D Lazio

099

How many times did Dynamo Kiev, AC Milan and Anderlecht each win the European Cup Winner's Cup?

A Four times

B Three times

C Twice

D Once

100

Which team were runners-up in both 1961 and 1967 but finally managed to win the title in 1972?

A Hamburg

B Fiorentina

C Rangers

D 1860 München

101

Three different Italian teams won the UEFA Cup in three consecutive years (1988-9, 1989-90 and 1990-1). Spot the odd one out:

    A Inter Milan

    B Parma

    C Napoli

    D Juventus

102

In the 1986 UEFA Cup Final, who did Real Madrid beat by 5-1 in the first leg, but lose to by 2-0 in the second leg?

    A Stuttgart

    B Espanol

    C IFK Göteborg

    D Cologne

103

In which round were Leeds United knocked out of the 2001-02 UEFA Cup?

    A Fourth round

    B Third round

    C Quarter-finals

    D Semi-finals

104

Who scored twice for Feyenoord in the 2002 UEFA Cup Final?

A Jon Dahl Tomasson
B Leonardo
C Pierre Van Hooijdonk
D Robin Van Persie

105

The 2001 UEFA Cup Final between Liverpool and Alaves was held where?

A Copenhagen
B Dortmund
C Paris
D Rotterdam

106

In which year did the traditional two-legged UEFA Cup Final permanently become a decisive single match fixture?

A 2000
B 1996
C 1994
D 1998

How many consecutive UEFA Cup wins did English clubs achieve between the late 1960s and early 1970s?

107

A Seven

B Five

C Four

D Six

How many years did the first UEFA Cup tournament (under its original name) last?

108

A Three

B Two

C Four

D One

How many tournament games were played during this time?

109

A 13

B 23

C 45

D 89

110

Which was the first Northern European club to claim
The Cup?

A IFK Göteborg

B Borussia Mönchengladbach

C Leeds United

D Anderlecht

Who were the African Champions in 1992?

111

- **A** Nigeria
- **B** Ivory Coast
- **C** Cameroon
- **D** Zaire

South American footballing nations belong to which confederation?

112

- **A** AFC
- **B** Conmebol
- **C** Concacaf
- **D** OFC

Which of the following is not a European football association/body?

113

- **A** Fédération Burkinabe de Football
- **B** Knattspyrnusanband Island
- **C** Federazione Sammarinese Giuoco Calcio
- **D** Magyar Labdarugo Szovetseg

114

Which country took football gold in the 14th Asian Games, 2002?

A South Korea

B Turkey

C Iran

D Japan

115

How often is the African Nations Cup held?

A Annually

B Every 5 years

C Every 4 years

D Every 2 years

116

Israel are members of which football confederation?

A CAF

B AFC

C UEFA

D CONCACAF

Why did South Africa pull out of the first African
Nations Cup?

117

A Because they were told to field a multi-racial team

B Due to severe civil unrest

C They couldn't afford to send a national squad

D Many of their players were farm workers, unable to
travel for extended periods

Which of the following nations does not belong to the OFC?

118

A Papua New Guinea

B Samoa

C Vanuatu

D Indonesia

How many member nations comprise the CAF

119

A 32

B 52

C 45

D 65

120 What is the Gaelic translation of the name of Aberdeen's ground, Pittodrie?

- **A** Hill of dung
- **B** Field of sheep
- **C** Sack of rotten vegetables
- **D** Pile of dirty undergarments

121 The Australian national football team are also known as what?

- **A** The Socceroos
- **B** The Billabongs
- **C** The Waltzing Matildas
- **D** The Sleepy Koalas

What did the Inter-Cities Fairs Cup become?

122

- **A** The World Cup
- **B** The European Champion Clubs' Cup
- **C** The European Cup Winners' Cup
- **D** The UEFA Cup

What did Tottenham Hotspur do in 1961, that Arsenal did in 1971 and Liverpool in 1986?

123

- **A** Won 'The Double'
- **B** Won the European Cup Winners' Cup
- **C** Won the Charity Shield
- **D** Won the Super Cup

Which of the following competitions was established first?

124

- **A** The European Cup Winners' Cup
- **B** The European Nations Cup
- **C** The African Nations Cup
- **D** The European Champion Clubs' Cup

125

Who scored the last ever goal in the European Cup Winners' Cup?

A Pavel Nedved

B Christian Vieri

C Dani

D Attillo Lombardo

126

UEFA Cup winners are entitled to keep a replica of the Cup. According to UEFA regulations, the dimensions of the replica should be what in proportion to the original cup?

A Same size

B 4/5 size

C 3/4 size

D 2/3 size

– Trophy Trivia –

The Jules Rimet Trophy was awarded to winners of what? **127**

- **A** The UEFA Cup
- **B** The World Cup
- **C** The FA Challenge Cup
- **D** The European Super Cup

How did 'Pickles' the dog achieve footballing fame? **128**

- **A** He scared off thieves that broke into the Manchester City trophy room
- **B** He was Liverpool's mascot during the 1970s
- **C** He brought the 1965 FA Cup Final to a temporary standstill by running onto the pitch
- **D** He recovered the stolen World Cup trophy in 1966

The original FA Cup was also known as what? **129**

- **A** The Little Tin Cup
- **B** The Little Tin Pot
- **C** The Little Tin Idol
- **D** The Little Tin Trophy

130

What happened to the Jules Rimet Trophy in 1970?

A FIFA voted to replace it with a new trophy

B It was damaged in transit to the World Cup Final

C Brazil were allowed to keep it for good, having won the World Cup three times

D It was stolen

In which year did the FA launch the English Premier League? **131**

A 1992
B 1991
C 1990
D 1994

Newcastle United set a Premier League record at the end of 1993-94 season by scoring how many goals in total? **132**

A 72
B 75
C 78
D 82

What was the 2001-02 Premiership called? **133**

A The FA Carling Premiership
B The FA Axa Premiership
C The FA Nationwide Premiership
D The FA Barclaycard Premiership

134 Who came out on top as the Premiership's leading goalscorer for 2001-02?

A Jimmy Floyd Hasselbaink

B Thierry Henry

C Mark Viduka

D Ruud Van Nistelrooy

135 At the end of the first Premiership season, which was the highest placed London club, finishing fifth in the new league?

A Queens Park Rangers

B Chelsea

C West Ham United

D Wimbledon

136 At the end of the 1997-8 season, which of the following teams just managed to escape relegation from the Premier League?

A Bolton Wanderers

B Crystal Palace

C Everton

D Barnsley

How many of the first ten Premiership titles were won by Manchester United?

137

- **A** 7
- **B** 6
- **C** 5
- **D** 4

Whose millions transformed Blackburn Rovers into a Premiership-winning side?

138

- **A** Jack Walker
- **B** Mike Walker
- **C** Johnnie Walker
- **D** Roy Walker

For which Premiership season did players first appear with their names on their shirts?

139

- **A** 1992/3
- **B** 1993/4
- **C** 1994/5
- **D** 1995/6

140

Who left the Manchester United subs bench to add to Nottingham Forest's misery by notching up four goals in the final ten minutes of a 1998-9 Premiership fixture, making the final score 8-1?

A Andy Cole

B Dwight Yorke

C Ole Gunnar Solskjaer

D Teddy Sheringham

In which year was football officially introduced as part of the Olympic Games?

141

- **A** 1896
- **B** 1908
- **C** 1904
- **D** 1900

Which country won Olympic gold for football in 1928?

142

- **A** Argentina
- **B** Belgium
- **C** Uruguay
- **D** France

Why did the Czechoslovakian team prematurely leave the pitch during the 1920 Olympic Games Final against Belgium?

143

- **A** To avoid humiliation as they were losing so badly
- **B** They believed the referee to be biased towards Belgium
- **C** Their manager ordered them from the pitch, following an argument with a FIFA official
- **D** In protest over a succession of dreadful tackles made by the Belgians

144

Why did an Olympic match between the USA and Italy erupt into pitch violence in 1936?

- **A** The Italians fielded a twelfth player when the referee had his back turned, and American substitutes attempted to drag him off
- **B** An Italian player was allowed to continue playing having refused to recognize the referee's sending-off decision
- **C** The losing Italian side persistently committed appalling tackles, unpunished by the German referee
- **D** An American player crushed the Italian goalkeeper during a corner kick

145

With three exceptions for each team, players competing in the Olympic Games football tournament must be under the age of what?

- **A** 23
- **B** 18
- **C** 21
- **D** 25

146

Which nation won the first Olympic football tournament, held in London in 1908?

- **A** Switzerland
- **B** Belgium
- **C** England
- **D** Sweden

Where was the first Women's World Cup tournament held?

147

- **A** USA
- **B** Canada
- **C** China
- **D** Sweden

Which nation walked away with the 1995 FIFA Women's World Cup title?

148

- **A** Norway
- **B** Germany
- **C** Denmark
- **D** USA

Who earned the title of (Women's) FIFA World Player of the Year 2002?

149

- **A** Mia Hamm
- **B** Gao Hong
- **C** Sun Wen
- **D** Birgit Prinz

150 Which team won the 2002 UEFA Women's Cup?

- **A** Toulouse FC
- **B** Umeå IK
- **C** FFC Frankfurt
- **D** HJK Helsinki

151 How many teams competed for the 2001-2 UEFA Women's Cup?

- **A** 33
- **B** 32
- **C** 25
- **D** 24

Norman Whiteside holds the record for being the youngest player to have done what?

152

A Scored in an FA Cup Final

B Appeared in an FA Cup Final

C Scored a Division 1 hat trick

D Scored in the Football League

What was the record-breaking World Cup match scoreline when Australia pounded American Samoa in 2001?

153

A 25-0

B 41-0

C 35-0

D 31-0

Which individual holds the record for having scored the most career goals?

154

A Franz Binder

B Pelé

C Artur Friedenreich

D Uwe Seeler

155

Which player received the accolade of scoring the first ever World Cup hat trick?

A Pedro Cea (Uruguay)

B Bart McGhee (USA)

C Guillermo Stábile (Argentina)

D Preguinho (Brazil)

156

The fastest ever hat trick was achieved by Independiente player Maglioni. How long did it take him to put three goals past the opposition's keeper?

A 7 minutes, 15 seconds

B 5 minutes, 10 seconds

C 3 minutes, 30 seconds

D 1 minute, 50 seconds

157

Vinnie Jones set a new record in 1991, being booked in record time. How much of the game had elapsed before the referee blew his whistle?

A 15 seconds

B 5 seconds

C 30 seconds

D 1 minute

158

In 2002, Hakan Sukur scored the fastest goal in World Cup history. How much of the game had elapsed before he put the ball into the back of the net?

A 10.8 seconds

B 20.8 seconds

C 30.8 seconds

D 1 minute, 8 seconds

159

France and Mexico contested the first ever World Cup match. What was the outcome of the game?

A France 1, Mexico 1

B France 2, Mexico 4

C France 3, Mexico 2

D France 4, Mexico 1

160

What do Tommy Smith, John Hollins, Steve Guppy and Peter Davenport all have in common?

A They have all won just one England Cap

B They all scored during their debut England games

C They were all sent off during their debut England games

D All have been England subs, but none of them have played in an international game

161

Family ties aside, what do Bobby Charlton and Jack Charlton have in common?

A They both played for England in the 1966 World Cup final

B They have sons named after each other

C Neither have played for more than one club

D Their wives are sisters

162

At what age did Alan Shearer retire from English international football?

A 28

B 30

C 29

D 31

163

Rio Ferdinand made his full England debut against which nation?

A Argentina

B Cameroon

C Holland

D Germany

164

By how much did Hungary, led by Ferenc Puskas, famously demolish the England team in 1953?

A Hungary 6, England 3

B Hungary 5, England 1

C Hungary 6, England 2

D Hungary 8, England 3

165

How many million pounds (UK sterling) was David Beckham sold to Real Madrid for by Manchester United?

A 20

B 25

C 30

D 35

166 Which team sings I'm Forever Blowing Bubbles?

  A Brighton
  B West Ham
  C Peterborough
  D Charlton

167 Who penned Coventry's team song Let's All Sing Together?

  A Sandie Shaw
  B Jimmy Greaves
  C Anthony Newley
  D Jimmy Hill

168 What is Liverpool's rousing team song?

  A Red is the Color
  B Glory Glory
  C Ferry 'Cross the Mersey
  D You'll Never Walk Alone

Which team sings Boing Boing Baggies, Boing Boing?

169

- **A** West Bromwich Albion
- **B** Port Vale
- **C** Celtic
- **D** Stoke City

Which year did Three Lions on a Shirt first hit No 1 in the UK charts as the team song for the European Cup?

170

- **A** 1992
- **B** 1994
- **C** 1996
- **D** 1998

What do Manchester City sing?

171

- **A** Blue is the Color
- **B** Blue Moon
- **C** The Locomotion
- **D** Blue Hotel

172 How many times have Brazil won the World Cup?

A 4
B 5
C 6
D 7

173 With which team formation did Brazil win the 1958 World Cup?

A 4-3-3
B 4-4-2
C 4-2-4
D 3-3-4

174 How many international goals did Pelé score during his playing career?

A 97
B 57
C 77
D 127

How old was Ronaldo when he first played an international game for Brazil?

175

    A 16

    B 19

    C 18

    D 17

Why was Pelé's first goal against Italy in the 1970 World Cup Final of particular significance?

176

    A It marked his 100th goal for Brazil

    B It marked Brazil's 100th World Cup goal

    C It was Pelé's first international goal against Italy

    D It came during Pelé's 100th Brazilian cap

Who did Brazil have to beat in their last World Cup qualifying game to ensure a place in the 2002 World Cup finals?

177

    A Costa Rica

    B Bolivia

    C Ecuador

    D Venezuela

178

In which of the following years did Argentina fail to reach the World Cup Final?

- **A** 1990
- **B** 1986
- **C** 1962
- **D** 1930

179

Of the entire 1978 Argentine World Cup team, who was the only member of the squad NOT playing for an Argentinian club?

- **A** Daniel Passarella
- **B** Leopoldo Luque
- **C** Osvaldo Ardiles
- **D** Mario Kempes

180

Which Argentinian became the first ever player to be sent off in a World Cup Final?

- **A** Pedro Monzon
- **B** Gustavo Dezotti
- **C** Diego Maradona
- **D** Omar Sivori

181

In how many of their eighteen World Cup 2002 qualifying games were Argentina victorious?

- **A** 10
- **B** 13
- **C** 15
- **D** 18

182

When four Celtic players were fined for their behavior in their World Club Championship game against Racing Club in 1967, what happened to their counterparts on the Argentinian team who were also sent off?

- **A** They were given large cash bonuses and new cars
- **B** They were imprisoned
- **C** They were given 3 months hard labor
- **D** They were exiled

183 Soviet goalkeeper, Lev Yashin, nearly substituted his soccer career in favor of which sport?

A Skiing

B Gymnastics

C Boxing

D Ice Hockey

184 Pelé's Brazilian debut at the age of 16 was against which nation?

A Paraguay

B Columbia

C Argentina

D Uruguay

185 How old was Stanley Matthews when he finally retired from playing football?

A 48

B 45

C 53

D 50

– Legends & Living Legends –

Portuguese legend, Eusebio, was born and brought up in which country? `186`

- **A** Angola
- **B** Mozambique
- **C** Brazil
- **D** Cape Verde

Who spearheaded Real Madrid's spate of European Cup wins in 1956, 1957, 1958, 1959 and 1960? `187`

- **A** Eusebio
- **B** Pelé
- **C** Alfredo Di Stefano
- **D** Ferenc Puskas

Which number was worn by Johan Cruyff for the greater part of his career with Ajax? `188`

- **A** 9
- **B** 10
- **C** 11
- **D** 14

189

When did Diego Maradona make his international debut?

A 1975
B 1979
C 1977
D 1981

190

A waxwork of which England hero was erected in Trafalgar Square during the 2002 World Cup?

A Bobby Moore
B Michael Owen
C Geoff Hurst
D David Beckham

In 1984 a take-over bid for Manchester United fell through. Which millionaire businessman put forward this bid?

191

A Sir Richard Branson

B Rupert Murdoch

C Robert Maxwell

D Sir Andrew Lloyd Weber

The title of 'Golden Eagle' is historically bestowed upon exceptional players belonging to which club?

192

A Boca Juniors

B Benfica

C Colo Colo

D Atletico Madrid

Who won the Moldovian football league 2001-02?

193

A Agro

B Happy End

C Zimbru Chisinau

D Serif

194

Nottingham Forest become the first British club to pay a £1 million ($1.5m) transfer fee to secure the talents of which player?

A John Robertson
B Viv Anderson
C Trevor Francis
D Peter Shilton

195

By what name were Manchester United formerly known?

A Singer's FC
B Ardwick FC
C Newton Heath
D Stanley

196

Arsenal Football Club was originally called 'Dial Square'. What was 'Dial Square'?

A The players' social club
B A workshop at the Royal Arsenal
C The name of the chairman's house
D The team's unusual attacking formation

Why were Sheffield United players aimlessly driven around in a bus before their home games in the late 30s?

197

- **A** To promote their home matches and increase attendance
- **B** The players believed that driving around the city three times would bring them luck
- **C** The United manager believed the trip would help them to relax
- **D** Because they were winning more away games than home games, club managers attributing this to the journey involved

In which country do the clubs Mika, Karabach, Lemagorts and Zvartnorts all compete?

198

- **A** Armenia
- **B** Albania
- **C** Croatia
- **D** Romania

What was a little unusual about a side fielded by Accrington Stanley during the 1950s?

199

- **A** All the players were Welsh
- **B** All the players were Irish
- **C** All the players were Scottish
- **D** All the players were French

200

What did a number of key Chelsea players refuse to do in 2001?

- **A** Travel to to Albania play a UEFA cup tie
- **B** Travel to Israel to play a UEFA cup tie
- **C** Accept new pay deals tabled by Chelsea
- **D** Play a Premiership fixture scheduled within two days of a French World Cup qualifying match

201

Why was Manchester City's draw against Stockport in October 2001 of significance to the club?

- **A** It was the first time they failed to beat Stockport at home
- **B** It was the first time they hadn't lost to Stockport at home
- **C** It was their 1500th competitive away game
- **D** It was their 1500th competitive game at Maine Road

202

Which non-league club fed their players a curious diet of sherry, glucose and eggs during their giant-slaying FA Cup performance in the late 1940s?

- **A** Worksop Town
- **B** Worcester City
- **C** Harrogate Town
- **D** Yeovil Town

Who once said: "It's bloody tough being a legend"?

203

- **A** Ron Atkinson
- **B** Geoff Hurst
- **C** Bill Shankly
- **D** George Best

Who once remarked of his teams' tactics: "We try to equalize before the others have scored"?

204

- **A** Jack Charlton
- **B** Danny Blanchflower
- **C** Graham Taylor
- **D** Jock Stein

Which England player declared: "Tackling is better than sex"?

205

- **A** Paul Gascoigne
- **B** Peter Beardsley
- **C** Paul Ince
- **D** Sol Campbell

206

"The boys done great" became whose catchphrase?

A Jimmy Hill

B Mick Channon

C Jimmy Greaves

D Alan Hansen

207

Who said: "It'd be great to see Wimbledon in Europe. Usually a small squad of players travel abroad followed by several thousand wild-eyed, drunken fans, wrecking wine bars and having running battles with the police. If Wimbledon get in there, it would be the other way round."

A Ian Wright

B Frank Skinner

C Vinnie Jones

D Margaret Thatcher MP

208

Who said: "You know what pleased me most of all? When the House of Commons voted me Beer Drinker of the Year"?

A Jack Charlton

B Paul Gascoigne

C Tony Adams

D Michael Owen

209

Who said: " When I first heard about Viagra, I thought it was a new player Chelsea had just signed"?

- **A** John Major MP
- **B** Ron Atkinson
- **C** Tony Banks MP
- **D** David Beckham

210

To whom was Gary Lineker referring when he commented: "...a strange bloke, irritated by everyone I think"?

- **A** Sven Goran Eriksson
- **B** Roy Keane
- **C** Stuart Pearce
- **D** Alex Ferguson

211

In reference to Fulham's considerable cash injection, who suggested: "With the kind of bankroll Kevin Keegan has been promised, even my old granny could get Fulham out of the second division"?

- **A** Alan Hansen
- **B** Ruud Gullit
- **C** Vinnie Jones
- **D** Mohamed Al-Fayed

212

Who suggested it wouldn't be such a bad thing if all footballers' agents were lined up against a wall and shot?

A Graham Taylor

B Howard Kendall

C Terry Venables

D George Graham

Where did the number 16 shirt worn by Fabien Barthez during France '98 end up?

213

A On a waxwork of the goalkeeper in Madame Tussaud's

B Hung above his parents' mantlepiece

C In the museum of French football

D In his grandfather's coffin

The skin of which animal is preferred for making the highest quality football boots?

214

A Goat

B Kangaroo

C Llama

D Camel

What are the colors of the AC Milan home strip?

215

A Red and black striped shirts, white shorts, black and red socks

B Black and white striped shirts, black shorts, black socks

C Black and white striped shirts, white shorts, white socks

D Red and black striped shirts, black shorts, black and red socks

216

In which year was it decided that goalkeepers should wear colors that would distinguish them from other players on the pitch?

A 1913
B 1898
C 1928
D 1943

217

What was unusual about the boots worn by Cameroon's Rigobert Song for the 1998 World Cup?

A They were unbranded
B Small wings of Achilles were attached to their outer sides
C They were heated
D One was yellow, one was red

218

What was the record-breaking figure guaranteed to Manchester United upon signing their kit deal with Umbro in 1994?

A £25m/$37.5m
B £20m/$30m
C £15m/$2.5m
D £10m/$15m

What do the two stars on Juventus's team shirt signify?

219

A The team's 100th anniversary, reached in 1997

B The achievement of winning five successive League titles

C The teams' contribution of players to World Cup winning teams

D The achievement of winning 20 League titles

Pelé's No. 10 shirt from the 1970 World Cup Final fetched how much at an auction in 2002?

220

A £157,750/$236.000

B £57,750/$86,000

C £257,750/$386,000

D £557,550$836,000

In preference to football boots, what did Celtic's 1930s signing, Abdul Salim, choose to wear on his feet?

221

A Moccasins

B Bandages

C Wellington boots

D Sandals

222

For what reason was a match between Sheffield and Glasgow briefly suspended in 1930 so that the referee could get his jacket?

A Fair weather gave way to a freak snowstorm

B His shirt color matched that of Sheffield's and players were mistakenly passing the ball to him

C He realized that he'd left his stopwatch in his jacket pocket

D A spectator ran onto the pitch and ripped off the official's shirt

Who was Charlie Faultless?

223

    A A center-back

    B A linesman

    C A goalkeeper

    D A referee

What nickname was given to Bolton Wanderers' daunting defense in the 1950s?

224

    A The Fearsome Four

    B The Ferocious Five

    C The Savage Six

    D The Terrible Trio

Who was born Edson Arantes do Nascimento?

225

    A Dunga

    B Didi

    C Pelé

    D Zico

226

Who were the Angels with Dirty Faces?

A Argentina's formidable attacking trio of the 1950s

B The Italian players accused of attempting to bribe their Polish opponent during the 1974 World Cup

C Argentina's 1986 World Cup side

D The Portuguese players that dogged Pelé with fierce tackles during the 1966 World Cup

227

Which victorious club were branded the 'Lisbon Lions' following their European Cup win in 1967?

A Newcastle United

B Rangers

C Chelsea

D Celtic

228

Which team were branded the Ale House Brawlers in the 1970s?

A Birmingham City

B Millwall

C Tottenham Hotspur

D Southampton

In which position did The Tiger and The Black Octopus play?

`229`

- **A** Center forward
- **B** Goal
- **C** Center-back
- **D** Full-back

Who were Carl Anton Wilhelm Hirschmann, Ludwig Sylow and Louis Muhlinghaus?

`230`

- **A** Representatives of the FIFA-founding nations
- **B** FIFA presidents
- **C** Referees in the first World Cup tournament
- **D** Belgian forwards in the 1938 World Cup squad

The 'Old Firm' refers to what?

`231`

- **A** The 1966 World Cup winning England team
- **B** The founding member clubs of the FA
- **C** Glasgow's two biggest football clubs, Celtic and Rangers
- **D** Sheffield FC

232 'El Beatle' became the affectionate nickname for whom?

- **A** George Best
- **B** Geoff Hurst
- **C** Ian Rush
- **D** Ian St. John

233 Brazilian legend Pelé was also known as what?

- **A** The Black Pearl
- **B** The Black Panther
- **C** The Black Diamond
- **D** The Black Fox

234 Who was referred to as 'Anfield Iron'?

- **A** Emlyn Hughes
- **B** Tommy Smith
- **C** Peter Beardsley
- **D** Bill Shankly

Stanley Matthews was christened with which nickname?

235

- **A** The Right-wing Wizard
- **B** The Dribbling Demon
- **C** The Wizard of Dribble
- **D** The Defensive Destroyer

John Barnes' nickname of 'Digger' was derived from which American TV show?

236

- **A** Dynasty
- **B** Dallas
- **C** Hart to Hart
- **D** Cagney and Lacey

Who was 'The Kaiser'?

237

- **A** Karl-Heinz Rummenigge
- **B** Gerd Müller
- **C** Franz Beckenbauer
- **D** Helmut Schön

238 Who was branded 'Psycho' for his style of play?

A Vinnie Jones

B Stuart Pearce

C Johnny Giles

D Gary Lineker

239 According to football fans, who might be branded a 'Bamber'?

A A fair-weather football enthusiast

B A player with too many qualifications for their own good

C A biased referee

D An irritating football commentator

240 William Foulke, Chelsea's enormous 23-stone goalie, was also known as what?

A Fatty Foulke

B Flabby Foulke

C Lardy Foulke

D Bulbous Billy

Leonidas Da Silva was the first player to win acclaim for his mastery of which footballing skill?

241

A The nutmeg

B The banana shot

C The bicycle kick

D The dry leaf

The term 'cut out' refers to which maneuver?

242

A To make a break with the ball

B To find a route through a seemingly impenetrable defense

C To block an opponent's pass

D To kick the ball out towards the edge of the penalty box from a corner

What was unusual about the throw-in style of Newcastle's Steve Watson?

243

A He performed a somersault before throwing the ball

B He only had one arm

C He threw the ball with his back to the players

D It was underarm

– Tricks of the Game –

244

What is a 'catenaccio'?

- **A** A defensive formation
- **B** A fluke goal
- **C** An overdramatized dive
- **D** A dummy move

245

Who scored a spectacular flying volley upon his England debut in 2002, securing a 1-1 draw against Holland?

- **A** Kieron Dyer
- **B** Trevor Sinclair
- **C** Darius Vassell
- **D** Owen Hargreaves

246

What was a little strange about the goal scored from a corner kick by Everton's Chedgzoy against Tottenham during the 1924-25 season?

- **A** He scored by dribbling the ball all the way from the corner and the goal was allowed
- **B** He passed the ball directly to a Tottenham player who instinctively put it into the back of the net
- **C** The ball was deflected into the goal off the referee and allowed
- **D** He flipped the ball into the air and headed it from the corner into the goal

What did Arsenal accuse Dynamo Moscow of doing when thick fog descended upon a fixture in 1945?

A Bringing an extra player onto the pitch

B Kidnapping the Arsenal defenders

C Swapping their goalkeeper

D Rotating their players and substitutes throughout the game

248 Which Italian team changed their name to Ambrosiana when fascist laws decreed their existing name to be unacceptable?

A Fiorentina

B Sampdoria

C Lazio

D Internazionale

249 Brazilian football club, Flamengo, was originally founded as a club for which activity?

A Dancing

B Rugby

C Rowing

D Swimming

250 What was Arsenal tube station called before being renamed in the clubs' honor in1932?

A Drayton

B Highbury Hill

C Gillespie Road

D St. Thomas

– All Change –

Who briefly assumed the role as England's caretaker-manager in 1999 and then again in 2000?

- **A** Ray Clemence
- **B** Glen Hoddle
- **C** Dave Sexton
- **D** Howard Wilkinson

What reason did Cameron Evans give for leaving Sheffield United after just 2 days, having transferred from Rangers in 1968?

- **A** He had an allergic reaction to the team shirts
- **B** He was homesick
- **C** His father had threatened to cut all ties upon discovering his son's transfer to an English club
- **D** He didn't want to move to Sheffield and commuting from Scotland proved too much

253

A world record transfer fee was paid when Alf Common moved from Sunderland to Middlesborough in 1905. How much did the Boro fork out?

- **A** £1000/$1500
- **B** £750/$1125
- **C** £500/$750
- **D** £2000/$3000

254

What did Roberto Baggio's record £8m/$12m Juventus signing lead to in 1990?

- **A** A takeover bid for Juventus by Silvio Berlusconi's Fininvest group
- **B** Riots in the street of Turin
- **C** A visit to Juventus by The Pope
- **D** Riots in the streets of Florence

255

Gary Lineker's signing to Barcelona set a new Spanish record. But how much did the England international cost the Spaniards?

- **A** £4.3m/$6.45
- **B** £3.5m/$5.25
- **C** £4.8m/$7.2
- **D** £5.4m/$8.1

Which Chinese club did Paul Gascoigne sign for in 2003?

256

A Gansu Tianma

B Shenyang Yinde

C Yunnan Hongta

D Chongqing Lifan

Chelsea paid a club record sum of £5m/$7.5m for Graeme Le Saux in 1997. But how much had they sold him for to Blackburn Rovers just four years earlier?

257

A £1,000,000/$1,500,000

B £800,000/$1,200,000

C £650,000/$975,000

D £500,000/$750,000

Rio Ferdinand became Britain's most expensive football player when he transferred from Leeds United to Manchester United. How much was the transfer fee negotiated between the two clubs?

258

A £35m/$52.5m

B £30m/$45m

C £25m/$37.5m

D £20m/$30m

259

And how much had Ferdinand cost Leeds United when he transferred from West Ham the previous year?

- **A** £18m/$27m
- **B** £16m/$24m
- **C** £14m/$21m
- **D** £12m/$18m

260

When Zinedine Zidane left Juventus for Real Madrid in 2001, a new transfer fee record was set. What was the deal worth?

- **A** £36.5m/$54.75m
- **B** £46.5m/$69.75m
- **C** £56.5m/$84.75m
- **D** £66.5m/$99.75m

261

Prior to the 2002 British transfer fee record paid for Juan Sebastian Veron, who had been Britain's most expensive import?

- **A** Nicolas Anelka
- **B** Ruud Van Nistelrooy
- **C** Jimmy Floyd Hasselbaink
- **D** Sylvain Wiltord

For which fictional team did the comic strip character 'Roy of the Rovers' play?

262

A Midchester Rovers

B Mudchester Rovers

C Milchester Rovers

D Melchester Rovers

Which movie saw Michael Caine and Sylvester Stallone starring alongside Pelé and Bobby Moore?

263

A The Great Game

B The Last Goal

C Fever Pitch

D Escape to Victory

Caricatures of Billy Meredith frequently featured which item in the player's mouth?

264

A A toothpick

B A cigarette

C A blade of grass

D A tin whistle

265

Jamie Redknapp is married to which pop starlet?

- **A** Dido
- **B** Emma Bunton
- **C** Louise
- **D** Nicole Appleton

266

What do comedians Norman Wisdom, Peter Sellers and Eric Morecambe have in common?

- **A** They have all played professional football
- **B** They have all served as board members of English football clubs
- **C** They were all Liverpool supporters
- **D** They were all referees prior to finding fame

267

What was the name of the 2002 film about an Asian girl who wants to be a professional footballer?

- **A** Bhaji on the Pitch
- **B** Bend it Like Beckham
- **C** A Shot at Glory
- **D** When Saturday Comes

Which Hollywood star became a director at Sheffield United in 2002?

`268`

A Kenneth Branagh

B Alan Rickman

C Sean Bean

D John Cleese

Following the 1998 World Cup in France, a poll by magazine Paris Match revealed who as being "the man most French women would like to spend their holidays with"?

`269`

A Ronaldo

B Thierry Henry

C Fabien Barthez

D Zinedine Zidane

Buster Bloodvessel (of Bad Manners) is the chairman of which seaside club?

`270`

A Brighton & Hove Albion

B Torquay United

C Southend United

D Margate

271

In 1997, Elle magazine voted which club as "Britain's hippest football team"?

A Arsenal
B Middlesborough
C Manchester United
D Liverpool

272

Who played football for Swiss club FC Auban prior to achieving Grand Prix stardom?

A Kimi Raikkonen
B Jacques Villeneuve
C Ralf Schumacher
D Michael Schumacher

273

Franz Beckenbauer asked which German star to join the Bayern Munich advisory board?

A Steffi Graf
B Bernhard Langer
C Boris Becker
D Claudia Schiffer

274

On which TV show did Ron Atkinson demonstrate his vocal prowess with a Frank Sinatra impersonation?

A Comic Relief

B Children in Need

C The Royal Variety Performance

D Stars in Their Eyes

275

Who made a guest appearance at Stirling Albion during half-time in a friendly match in 1954?

A Roy Rogers and Trigger

B Mickey Mouse and Donald Duck

C Elvis

D The Moscow State Circus

276 Which football stadium has the largest spectator capacity in Europe?

A Estadio da Luz
B Nou Camp
C Santiago Bernabeu
D Luzhniki Stadium

277 Where is the József Bozsik stadium?

A Budapest
B Prague
C Warsaw
D Zagreb

278 Which English football ground is said to be haunted by a ghost called Fred?

A Brammall Lane
B Goodison Park
C Craven Cottage
D Boundary Park

Which movie star has a stadium named after him?

279

- **A** Al Pacino
- **B** Robert De Niro
- **C** Arnold Schwarzenegger
- **D** Sean Connery

The King Baudouin Stadium is overlooked by which landmark?

280

- **A** Vajdahunyad Castle
- **B** The Spacetower
- **C** The Sacre Coeur
- **D** The Atomium

The Vicente Calderón Stadium is situated where?

281

- **A** Barcelona
- **B** Madrid
- **C** Seville
- **D** Valencia

282

Which of the following statements is true?

A Maine Road was originally Manchester United's home ground

B Stamford Bridge was originally Fulham's home ground

C Anfield was originally Everton's home ground

D Meadow Lane was originally Nottingham Forest's home ground

283

In which stadium would you find the famous Ultra Sur stand?

A Azteca

B Nou Camp

C Centenario

D Santiago Bernabeu

284

By what name was Wembley Stadium originally known?

A The King's Stadium

B The National Stadium

C The Empire Stadium

D The Colonial Stadium

Turkish football club Galatasaray are at home in which stadium?

285

- **A** Inönü Stadi
- **B** Fenerbahçe Stadyum
- **C** Atatürk Stadium
- **D** Ali Sami Yen Stadyum

What unusual feature adorns a corner of Goodison Park?

286

- **A** A water fountain
- **B** A library
- **C** A church
- **D** A statue of Queen Mary

For what is the Centenario stadium famed?

287

- **A** Having the greatest crowd capacity of any stadium in the world
- **B** Staging the first ever World Cup Final
- **C** Being the most expensive stadium in the world to build
- **D** Having the highest altitude of any stadium in the world

288

The rebuilding of Wembley Stadium is being financed by a bank from which country?

A Netherlands

B USA

C Switzerland

D Germany

289

How was Hartlepool's ground destroyed in 1916?

A By a fire that started in a chestnut vendor's cart

B It collapsed following a minor earth tremor

C Bombs were dropped on it by German zeppelins

D It was dismantled so that the materials could be used to make munitions

290

In 1963, Halifax Town's ground was put to a rather different use? What did it become for a short time?

A A mud wrestling arena

B A stunt bike park

C An ice rink

D An international egg-and-spoon race venue

What were soldiers ordered to do at Wembley Stadium just days before its gates opened to the public?

A Simulate a pitch invasion

B Test the strength of the structure by marching up and down

C Dispose of an ammunition dump, discovered whilst laying the pitch

D Assist builders in completing the stadium in time for its official opening

292 How did West Bromich Albion acquire their nickname "The Baggies"?

A The name was coined in reference to the team's Scottish contingent of the early days

B The club was originally an army team and players left their haversacks or 'bags' next to the touchline when they played

C It referred to the high number of games the club won – or bagged – during their first ever season

D The players were foundry workers and wore baggy trousers called 'baggies' in their line of work

293 By what nickname are Millwall known?

A The Lions

B The Tigers

C The Terriers

D The Stags

294 Who were once known as The Biscuitmen?

A Accrington Stanley

B Lincoln City

C Reading

D Halifax Town

Why are Walsall also known as The Saddlers?

295

A The club was originally a jockey club

B The town has a history of saddle-making

C The club was originally a cycling club

D They became renowned for alternating between Divisions two and three, consistently sitting either at the top of three or bottom of two

Norman Hallam, who played for Port Vale, Halifax and Barnsley, was the only postwar professional player to have which title?

296

A Lord

B Earl

C Sir

D Reverend

297

Who did Manchester United face just prior to the tragic plane crash in 1958 that claimed the lives of eight United players?

A Bayern Munich

B Real Madrid

C Milan

D Red Star Belgrade

298

What was the cause of the commotion that led to the death of 66 fans at Ibrox Park during a Rangers/Celtic match in 1971?

A A last minute goal, causing departing fans to return to the terraces

B A terrace collapsing under the weight of jubilant fans

C Conflict between a small group of fans resulting in a crowd surge

D A fire on the terraces

299

Which two teams were playing at Hillsborough on the disastrous day that cost the lives of 95 fans?

A Liverpoool and Sheffield Wednesday

B Liverpool and Nottingham Forest

C Liverpool and Manchester United

D Sheffield Wednesday and Nottingham Forest

In which year did the Heysel disaster occur?

300

A 1983

B 1984

C 1985

D 1986

What was the title of Jimmy Greaves' first autobiography, revealing his addiction to alcohol?

301

A Honey I drunk the savings

B This one's on me

C Life's a blur

D Can't believe I hit the bar again

302

In which year was FIFA founded?

A 1908

B 1904

C 1900

D 1896

303

Whose FIFA presidency began in 1961?

A Sir Stanley Rous

B Arthur Drewry

C Rodolphe Seeldrayers

D Jules Rimet

304

Which of the following countries were not involved in the inauguration of FIFA?

A Denmark

B France

C England

D Switzerland

– FIFA Facts –

How long does a standard FIFA presidential term last? `305`

- A One year
- B Five years
- C Two years
- D Four years

Who was elected as FIFA's first president? `306`

- A Jules Rimet
- B Daniel Burley Woolfall
- C Robert Guérin
- D Rodolphe William Seeldrayers

Representatives from each of FIFA's founding member countries first met in which European city? `307`

- A Paris
- B Geneva
- C Brussels
- D Copenhagen

308 Jules Rimet, World Cup mastermind, was nominated for what?

A The Booker Prize

B French Presidency

C An Academy Award

D The Nobel Peace Prize

309 When did the first non-European football association join FIFA?

A 1906

B 1909

C 1912

D 1915

310 Which country did this association represent?

A South Africa

B USA

C Argentina

D Chile

FIFA banned its members from playing which English club when they expressed a desire to play in Europe, against the wishes of the English FA?

311

- **A** The English Ramblers
- **B** The English Rumblers
- **C** The English Bumblers
- **D** The English Mumblers

Representatives from each of FIFA's founding member countries first met in which European city?

312

- **A** Copenhagen
- **B** Geneva
- **C** Brussels
- **D** Paris

313 How did Rangers win the Glasgow Charity Cup Final in 1930?

    A At the toss of a coin

    B By the consensus of match officials

    C The Celtic team didn't turn up and Rangers were declared the winners

    D On penalties

314 Who created a new Scottish League record for scoring in the most consecutive games in the 1997-98 season?

    A Ally McCoist

    B Henrik Larsson

    C Rod Wallace

    D Marco Negri

315 At which Scottish ground did experienced referee Hugh Dallas infamously get struck by a coin thrown from the crowd?

    A Parkhead

    B Ibrox

    C Celtic Park

    D Tannadice

Which Scottish football club are known as the 'Diamonds?'

316

A Dundee United

B Airdrieonians

C Partick Thistle

D St. Johnstone

Which Rangers fan made his debut for Celtic in 1970?

317

A Billy McNeill

B Kenny Dalglish

C Graeme Souness

D Tommy Gemmell

From what does the Scottish football team 'Heart of Midlothian' derive its unusual name?

318

A A clipper owned by a wealthy Scottish nobleman

B Edinburgh Castle

C A heart-shaped diamond belonging to the Scottish monarchy

D An old prison in Edinburgh

319

Who are the 'Tartan Army'?

A The Scottish national football team

B The Scottish squad that beat England at Wembley in 1977

C Dedicated Scottish fans that follow Scotland across the globe

D A rock band that dress up as celebrated Scottish football players when they perform

320

Inveresk in Scotland played host to an unusual match between whom in the 17th Century?

A Red-haired women and dark-haired women

B Scottish women and English women

C Married women and unmarried women

D Housewives and farmer's wives

321

Who famously raised Scotland's hopes of progressing to the second round of the World Cup finals for the first time by chipping a third Scottish goal over the Dutch keeper in 1978?

A Archie Gemmill

B Joseph Jordan

C Kenny Dalglish

D Lou Macari

What was unusual about the Scottish Cup tie between Falkirk and Inverness Thistle in the late 1970s?

A It was played at night by the light of a full moon, a power failure having knocked out the floodlights

B Stoppage time took the length of the game in excess of three hours

C The entire Inverness team were sent off following a heated dispute argument with the referee

D It was postponed 29 times

323 How many goals did Just Fontaine score for France during the 1958 World Cup finals?

- **A** 16
- **B** 7
- **C** 10
- **D** 13

324 Who led France to the 1992 European Championship finals?

- **A** Gerard Houllier
- **B** Michel Platini
- **C** Michel Haldigo
- **D** Jacques Santini

325 Frenchman Lucien Laurent was the first player to do what?

- **A** Score a goal in a World Cup match
- **B** Captain France to a European Championship title
- **C** Receive a yellow card during a World Cup match
- **D** Score a golden goal in a World Cup match

Who scored both the French goals needed to stop Croatia from progressing in the 1998 World Cup Final?

326

A Emmanuel Petit

B Youri Djorkaeff

C Lillian Thuram

D Lauren Blanc

327 What is the translation from Afrikaans of South African born goalkeeper Bruce Grobbelaar's surname?

A Clumsy

B Trustworthy

C Heroic

D Tall man

328 A lifetime ban was imposed on Fulham's George Parsonage for doing what?

A Requesting a £50/$75 signing-on fee from Chesterfield

B Openly criticizing the FA

C Leaving the pitch following a dispute with a referee

D Critically injuring an opponent with an appalling tackle

329 Which of these French clubs didn't Eric Cantona play for during his career?

A Martigues

B Brest

C Auxerre

D Bordeaux

Who was Manchester United's top goalscorer for the 1998-99 FA Premiership season?

330

A Ole Gunnar Solskjaer

B David Beckham

C Dwight Yorke

D Andy Cole

What have Alfredo Di Stefano, Ladislav Kubala and Jim Kennaway all done?

331

A Played in the USA towards the end of their careers

B Won caps playing for more than one country

C Coached European national teams

D Spent time in prison for their political views

In 1979, with which team did Dutch footballer Ruud Gullit embark upon his footballing career?

332

A FC Utrecht

B PSV Eindhoven

C Haarlem

D Feyenoord

333

In February 1970, George Best returned to football following a month-long suspension to do what?

A Receive a red card within the first 5 minutes

B Set a new FA Cup record by scoring six goals in a single match

C Sustain an injury, preventing him playing for a further month

D Score an own goal

334

Robbie Keane scored two goals against which team upon his debut for Wolverhampton Wanderers?

A Ipswich Town

B Norwich

C Middlesborough

D West Bromich Albion

335

When a referee booked Bristol's Mike Bagley for being abusive, what was the player's reaction?

A He ate the referee's notebook

B He stripped off and ran around the pitch naked

C He removed his boots and threw them at the referee

D He dragged the referee to the dressing room and locked him in

What happened to Fulham's Rodney Marsh when he sealed victory against Leicester with a header in 1963?

336

A His two front teeth were knocked out by the impact

B He was attacked by a linesman who was a Leicester City supporter

C He was left permanently deaf by the impact

D He was mobbed by Fulham fans and stripped of his clothes

What did Wolverhampton Wanderers' player, Tom Phillipson, become after his footballing days had ended?

337

A Shadow Defense Secretary

B An Grand National-winning jockey

C Lord Mayor of the city

D A woman

Prior to embarking on his footballing career, Chris Waddle made what for a living?

338

A Sausages

B Ornamental ducks

C Hats

D Dartboards

339

The highest recorded spectator attendance was witnessed in 1950 at a Brazil-Uruguay World Cup match. What was the official attendance figure?

- A 199,589
- B 202,435
- C 205,326
- D 208,221

340

Hat-trick record holder, Dixie Dean, scored how many hat-tricks during his League career?

- A 28
- B 40
- C 34
- D 46

341

In 1994, Roger Milla became the oldest player to participate in a World Cup finals. How old was he at the time?

- A 42
- B 40
- C 44
- D 46

How many nations took part in the 1998 World Cup finals?

342

A 32

B 28

C 24

D 36

A record-breaking club sponsorship deal was agreed between communications company O2 and which English club in April 2002?

343

A Leeds United

B Aston Villa

C Chelsea

D Arsenal

What was England's biggest win at Wembley Stadium?

344

A 6 - 0

B 7 - 1

C 9 - 0

D 8 - 2

345

Sunderland's embarrassing defeat at the hands of non-League Yeovil Town in 1949 attracted which odds at the bookmakers?

- **A** 1000-1
- **B** 500-1
- **C** 5000-1
- **D** 100-1

346

Goalkeeper Peter Shilton holds the record for having won the most England caps. How many did he have?

- **A** 118
- **B** 120
- **C** 130
- **D** 125

347

The FA signed an eight-year sponsorship deal with Umbro in 2002. What was this deal worth?

- **A** £80m/$120m
- **B** £120m/$180m
- **C** £160m/$240m
- **D** £200m/$300m

For how long was Selwyn Baptiste of Trinidad suspended when it was discovered that he had broken an existing ban imposed to stop him from playing?

348

- **A** 1000 years
- **B** 20 years
- **C** 100 years
- **D** 10 years

349 How many goals did England's goalkeeper, Gordon Banks, concede during the 1966 World Cup campaign?

A 7

B 1

C 5

D 3

350 Geoff Hurst entered the record books in the 1966 World Cup for doing what?

A Being the first ever player to score a hat trick in a World Cup Final

B Scoring the earliest ever goal in a World Cup Final

C Being the first player in World Cup history to score in every team match from the first round to the final

D Being the first ever player to be sent off during a World Cup Final

351 When England won the 1966 World Cup, the gap since a host nation had last won the tournament was how long?

A 32 years

B 28 years

C 24 years

D 16 years

Which of the following teams were not in England's group for the 1966 World Cup?

352

A Mexico

B Uruguay

C Portugal

D France

Who scored Germany's late equalizer during the 1966 World Cup Final?

353

A Wolfgang Overath

B Wolfgang Weber

C Helmet Haller

D Franz Beckenbauer

Who uttered the immortal words: "Some people are on the pitch, they think it's all over... It is now!"?

354

A Kenneth Wolstenholme

B Kenneth Wolfenstein

C Kenneth Wolstenhurst

D Jimmy Greaves

355

What was the final outcome of the 1966 World Cup Final?

A England 3, Germany 1

B England 4, Germany 2

C England 3, Germany 2

D England 4, Germany 3

356

England managed to beat all bar one of the teams that they faced during the 1966 tournament. Which country managed to hold the home nation to a draw?

A France

B Uruguay

C Mexico

D Argentina

357

From whom did Bobby Moore collect the coveted Jules Rimet trophy upon England's victory?

A Harold Wilson

B The Queen Mother

C The Duke of Edinburgh

D The Queen

Other than Geoff Hurst, who also scored for England in the 1966 World Cup Final?

A Roger Hunt

B Alan Ball

C Bobby Moore

D Martin Peters

359 Brian Clough's notoriously short-lived management of Leeds lasted how long?

A 44 days
B 33 days
C 21 days
D 4 days

360 Who did George Graham manage prior to moving to Arsenal?

A West Ham United
B Charlton Athletic
C Millwall
D Fulham

361 England's giant-slaying performance, including their much celebrated 4-1 victory over Holland, during the Euro '96 tournament was overseen by whom?

A Bobby Robson
B Terry Venables
C Graham Taylor
D Howard Wilkinson

What happened during England's first away game under the management of Terry Venables?

362

A The match was abandoned after 27 minutes due to crowd trouble

B The match was abandoned after 27 minutes due to exceptionally bad weather

C The referee was injured and had to be replaced

D England lost 3-0

Which vegetable was superimposed onto England Manager Graham Taylor's head by a British national tabloid newspaper?

363

A A cabbage

B A beetroot

C A turnip

D A potato

Which TV chef became a director of Norwich football club in 1997?

364

A Ainsley Harriott

B Jamie Oliver

C Delia Smith

D Antony Worrall Thompson

365

Which manager was renowned for presenting a football to his team before the start of a game and telling them: "This is what we play with. Go and get it!"?

A Gordon Strachan

B Joe Kinnear

C Harry Redknapp

D Brian Clough

366

Allan Mullery, Peter Taylor and Brian Clough have all managed one of the following clubs. Which one?

A Stoke City

B Brighton & Hove Albion

C Rotherham United

D Walsall

367

Who was Queens Park Rangers' manager in 1995?

A Gerry Francis

B Stewart Houston

C Don Howe

D Ray Wilkins

Why did Stockport County fire their manager in 1974?

368

A Because he refused to change his car for a new one in the club's colors

B Because they discovered he had been attending Oldham Athletic games as a fan

C Because he lived too far from the club

D Because he took the team on a drunken binge the night before a match

369

When did the referee's whistle first make an appearance in football?

A 1918
B 1908
C 1898
D 1878

370

Brazilian referee, Arnaldo Coelho, became the highest paid referee of his time when he oversaw the 1982 World Cup Final. How much did he earn for his services during the game?

A £500/$750
B £250/$375
C £1000/$1500
D £1500/$2250

371

If the assistant referee holds his flag in both hands, above his head, what is he indicating to the referee?

A A goal kick should be awarded
B A substitution is ready to take place
C A corner kick should be awarded
D The match half has exceeded its length or its specified period of time added on

What was officially introduced into the game of football in 1891?

- **A** The penalty
- **B** The offside rule
- **C** The corner kick
- **D** The drop ball

373

What is the minimum acceptable length of a professional soccer field?

A 130 yards (120m)
B 120 yards (110m)
C 110 yards (100m)
D 100 yards (90m)

374

What is the maximum acceptable width of a professional soccer field?

A 50 yards (45m)
B 60 yards (55m)
C 100 yards (90m)
D 70 yards (64m)

375

A flagpost must be a minimum of how many feet in height?

A 4 feet
B 7 feet
C 6 feet
D 5 feet

What is the official inside measurement between goalposts?

- **A** 6.62 meters/21.7 feet
- **B** 7.32 meters/24 feet
- **C** 7.62 meters/25 feet
- **D** 6.92 meters/22.7 feet

377

Who was voted European Footballer of the Year, 1972?

- **A** Gordon Banks
- **B** Johan Cruyff
- **C** Franz Beckenbauer
- **D** Gerd Müller

378

The European Footballer of the Year accolade has been awarded to just one player in three successive years. Who?

- **A** Kevin Keegan
- **B** Johan Cruyff
- **C** Marco van Basten
- **D** Michel Platini

379

Who was the first footballer to twice receive the accolade of World Footballer of the Year?

- **A** Roberto Baggio
- **B** Marco Van Basten
- **C** Ronaldo
- **D** Lothar Matthäus

– Awards –

Where do Bobby Moore's England caps and World Cup winners' medal now reside?

- **A** In a Bank of England vault
- **B** Fulham's home ground
- **C** The Victoria and Albert Museum
- **D** West Ham's home ground

Which FIFA award is presented at the end of a World Cup tournament to the best goalkeeper?

- **A** The Zubizaretta Award
- **B** The Maier Award
- **C** The Yashin Award
- **D** The Banks Award

Who won this award the first time it was presented?

- **A** Peter Schmeichel
- **B** Michel Preud'homme
- **C** Fabien Barthez
- **D** Taffarel

383

If two or more players are tied for the title of top goalscorer at the end of a World Cup tournament, which additional factor is taken into account to determine who should receive the award?

A How many of the goals were penalties

B The number of bookings that the player received during the tournament

C The final position that the player's team finished in the tournament

D How many additional goals were scored as a direct result of the player's assistance

384

Which legend picked up the FIFA Player of the Century Award in 2000?

A Alfredo Di Stefano

B Diego Maradona

C Pelé

D Stanley Matthews

385

Which club was crowned FIFA Club of the Century in 2000?

A Manchester United

B Bayern Munich

C Real Madrid

D FC Barcelona

Which award was presented to the top goalscorer at the end of the 2002 World Cup tournament?

386

A The Adidas Golden Boot

B The Adidas Golden Shoe

C The Adidas Golden Slipper

D The Adidas Golden Stud

Who was voted (men's) FIFA World Player of the Year, 2002?

387

A Oliver Kahn

B Zinedine Zidane

C Luis Figo

D Ronaldo

Prior to Michael Owen winning European Footballer of the Year in 2001, how many British footballers had been crowned with the title?

388

A Five

B Three

C Seven

D One

389 Which former England Manager picked up an OBE in the 2002 New Year Honor's List?

- **A** Terry Venables
- **B** Bobby Robson
- **C** Graham Taylor
- **D** Ron Greenwood

Barcelona football club granted honorary membership to whom in 1982?

`390`

- **A** Margaret Thatcher
- **B** Pope John Paul II
- **C** Al Pacino
- **D** Julio Iglesias

Which variety of bird-brained supporter regularly traveled by bus to watch Nottingham Forest matches?

`391`

- **A** A green woodpecker
- **B** A jay
- **C** A rook
- **D** A jackdaw

'What a Load of Cobblers' is the fanzine for which club?

`392`

- **A** Huddersfield Town
- **B** Luton Town
- **C** Stoke City
- **D** Northampton Town

393 How many spectators watched Rushden & Diamonds inaugural match in 1992?

- **A** 315
- **B** 15
- **C** 515
- **D** 1015

394 Who streaked across the pitch during a Middlesborough/Newcastle United game to get her hands on Paul Gascoigne?

- **A** Erica Roe
- **B** Vanessa Richards
- **C** Vanessa Roe
- **D** Sheila Nicholls

395 Why did the Middlesborough team cheer one of their fans following a fixture in 1895?

- **A** He scored, having been called upon to play when Middlesborough were found to be one player short
- **B** He was celebrating his 100th birthday
- **C** He was the only fan that bothered to travel to the game
- **D** He treated the team to meat pies and ale after their match victory

396

How did Mauritian Manchester City fan, Moussa Balagobin, meet misfortune when he traveled thousands of miles to see his favorite club play?

A He was arrested on suspicion of drugs trafficking

B He was imprisoned as a suspected illegal immigrant

C He went to the wrong ground – Manchester United's – and missed the game

D He was mugged for his Manchester City shirt, shorts and socks on the way to the game

397

Tottenham Hotspur fans occasionally dress to attend games as a trio of what?

A Blind mice

B Angels

C Musketeers

D Wise men

398

What was the name of Grimsby Town's inflatable fishy mascot that floated around the terraces in the 1980s?

A Harry the Haddock

B Lawrence the Lobster

C Colin the Cod

D Charlie the Crayfish

399

If Lenny the Lion, Kingsley the Lion and Lofty Lion all got together for a knock-about in the park, which of the following clubs would not be represented amongst the three lions?

A Bolton Wanderers

B Reading

C York

D Shrewsbury Town

400

Who was the official mascot for the 1986 World Cup tournament in Mexico?

A Gauchito

B Naranjito

C Juanito

D Pique

Swansea's Cyril the Swan hit the sports headlines by doing what to Millwall's Zampa the Lion?

401

A Dragging him along the touchline by the tail

B Stamping on his head

C Drop-kicking his head into the crowd

D Rugby-tackling him over the goal line

Peterborough's mascot, aptly named Peter Burrow, is what type of animal?

402

A A rabbit

B A badger

C A mole

D A vole

Marvin the Moose can be seen on the rampage whenever which team are playing?

403

A Cambridge United

B Burnley

C Crewe Alexandra

D Oxford United

404

How did Charlton's Keith Peacock make history when he played against Bolton during the 1965-66 season?

A He was the youngest player to appear in a League game

B He was the first ever player to come on as a substitute

C He came on as a substitute and was injured in record time

D He was the first professional referee to play as a professional footballer

405

Billy Wright was the first British player to do what?

A Win 100 caps

B Transfer to a European club

C Captain a European Championship-winning England team

D Captain England at the age of 21

406

Aberdeen's home ground was the first to have what?

A A dug-out

B Advertising hoardings

C A VIP box

D A heated pitch

Who scored France's 1000th international goal?

407

- **A** Youri Djorkaeff
- **B** Didier Deschamps
- **C** Thierry Henry
- **D** Emmanuel Petit

Which was the first English club to win 'The Double'?

408

- **A** Preston North End
- **B** Manchester City
- **C** Arsenal
- **D** Orient FC

In 1878, the first football match to be played at night by artificial light was held where?

409

- **A** Coventry
- **B** London
- **C** Birmingham
- **D** Sheffield

410

Which club were the first to feature a sponsor's name on their shirt?

- **A** Kettering Town
- **B** Leyton Orient
- **C** Bolton Wanderers
- **D** Chertsey Town

411

Which two teams contested the centenary FA Cup Final in 1981?

- **A** Tottenham Hotspur and Aston Villa
- **B** Manchester City and Tottenham Hotspur
- **C** Manchester City and Aston Villa
- **D** Liverpool and Southampton

412

When was the white football officially introduced?

- **A** 1955
- **B** 1951
- **C** 1959
- **D** 1963

Who was the first football league transfer worth four figures (£1000/$1500) and became the subject of a heated debate in the House of Commons?

A Stanley Matthews

B Tom Finney

C Clem Stephenson

D Alf Common

414

How many times was Stanley Matthews booked during his 33-year-long career?

A Once
B Three times
C Never
D Five times

415

When Turkey's Hakan Unsal kicked the ball at Rivaldo's legs during a 2002 World Cup game, which part of his body did the Brazilian player dramatically clutch to ensure that his assailant was booked?

A His stomach
B His groin
C His face
D His calf

416

What was the ultimatum given to Soviet team, Start FC, should they beat the German army team, Flakelf?

A They would be shot
B They would be imprisoned
C They would be sent to Siberia
D They would be flogged

– Fair Play –

417

Who holds the infamous title of being the first player to be dismissed during a World Cup fixture?

A Maurice Pinel (France)

B Luis Monti (Argentina)

C Aleksandar Tirnanic (Yugoslavia)

D Mario De Las Casas (Peru)

418

Who was made to undertake community service in 1995?

A Roy Keane

B Paul Gascoigne

C Vinnie Jones

D Eric Cantona

419

In 1905, Billy Meredith, Manchester City's captain, was banned from playing for an entire season. Why?

A For accepting a bribe to underperform during an important game

B For attempting to bribe Aston Villa's Captain towards the end of the 1904-05 season

C For attempting to bribe the referee prior to a crucial game close to the end of the 1904-05 season

D For placing a large bet on his own team to lose their penultimate game of the 1904-05 season

420 Why was Diego Maradona banned from football for 15 months in 1994?

- **A** He tested positive for drugs
- **B** He lunged at an opposing player who had committed a foul on him
- **C** He pushed a referee aside having been shown a red card
- **D** He attacked a photographer and smashed his camera

421 Why was Portuguese player Joao Pinto punished with a six-month club and national ban in 2002?

- **A** For punching an opponent who was pulling his shirt
- **B** For spitting at an opponent who had fouled him
- **C** For punching a referee, having been shown the red card
- **D** For kicking the ball from a referee's hands

422 Why was Leicester City's Johnny Morris suspended for two weeks in 1957?

- **A** For suggesting that a referee needed glasses
- **B** For punching the ball from a referee's hands
- **C** For snatching and tearing up a red card that was shown to him
- **D** For snatching a referee's whistle and blowing it

423

Which type of musical instrument resulted in a booking for Birmingham City's Liam Daish when he simulated playing a replica during a game?

A Trumpet

B Didgeridoo

C Guitar

D Violin

424

The curious sporting headline 'Queen in brawl at Palace' appeared in which British national newspaper?

A The Sun

B The Guardian

C The Times

D The Mirror

425 Gillingham striker Marlon King was jailed in 2002 for what?

- **A** Aggravated burglary
- **B** Tax evasion
- **C** Handling a stolen vehicle
- **D** Credit card fraud

426 In 1998 Terry Venables was banned from doing what for seven years?

- **A** Managing a football team
- **B** Being a company director
- **C** Coaching a football team
- **D** Driving

427 Why were Leeds players Jonathan Woodgate and Lee Bowyer in disgrace and in the headlines in 2001?

- **A** For brawling with Tottenham players
- **B** For a drinking binge that resulted in a car crash
- **C** For an alleged assault on an Asian student
- **D** For match fixing

– Law and Disorder –

428

What happened at the request of the Argentinian president following Milan's 1969 World Club Cup victory over Estudiantes in Buenos Aires?

A The entire Milanese team were arrested and deported

B Three of the Estudiantes players were imprisoned

C Several Estudiantes players were banned for life

D Argentinian clubs were barred from playing Italian clubs

429

Why was Bradford player Benito Carbone fined £80,000/$120,000 by his own club in 2002?

A For vandalising a changing room in a fit of temper

B For refusing to play as a substitute

C For missing training sessions

D For refusing to play in a different position

430

Why was Eric Cantona banned from playing football for eight months in 1995?

A For kung-fu kicking an abusive fan

B For throwing a coin that hit him on the head back into the crowd

C For punching an abusive fan

D For grasping an abusive fan in a headlock and dragging him from the crowd

431

Who were Manchester United playing when this incident took place?

A Blackburn Rovers

B Charlton Athletic

C Crystal Palace

D Coventry City

432

Referred to as the Bogotá Incident, what was Bobby Moore accused of stealing during the 1970 World Cup tournament?

A A hotel bathrobe

B A car

C An expensive bracelet

D A gold watch

Shortly after signing for Internazionale, team doctors discovered that Kanu suffered from what?

433

- **A** A heart defect
- **B** Asthma
- **C** Diabetes
- **D** Epilepsy

Which injury very nearly prevented David Beckham from playing in the 2002 World Cup finals?

434

- **A** A fractured metatarsal
- **B** Groin strain
- **C** A hamstring injury
- **D** Achilles tendinitis

Dennis Bergkamp has a fear of what?

435

- **A** Enclosed spaces
- **B** Large crowds
- **C** Flying
- **D** Spiders

436 Which severe illness did Garrincha overcome as a child before progressing to become a Brazilian soccer star?

A Polio

B Malaria

C Typhoid

D Diphtheria

437 What brought Dion Dublin's career with Manchester United to a premature end, having played just 12 games for the club?

A A broken leg

B A broken collar bone

C An eye infection

D An argument with Alex Ferguson

438 Who was rushed to hospital for emergency heart surgery in 2001 during a Liverpool v Leeds United match?

A The referee

B David O'Leary

C Phil Thompson

D Gerard Houllier

What was thrown at the referee during Millwall's fierce encounter with Birmingham City in January 2002?

439

A A smoked haddock

B A rubber chicken

C A meat pie

D A butternut squash

'The Battle of Berne' marked a notorious encounter between which two teams?

440

A Hungary and Argentina

B Brazil and Argentina

C Hungary and Brazil

D Italy and Brazil

441

What happened when Argentinian team Wanderers staged a sit-down protest in the middle of a game?

A The referee booked the entire team and then went home

B They were arrested for staging an illegal protest

C Angry fans carried them from the stadium and threw them into a nearby river

D The opposition took advantage and scored 71 goals

442

What did Nobby Stiles routinely do before playing a game?

A Remove his hearing aid

B Remove his false teeth

C Kiss his lucky piece of turf

D Walk around the dressing-room three times backwards

443

Who ran a World Wildlife Fund shop on a part-time basis during his early footballing days?

A Peter Schmeichel

B David Ginola

C Zinedine Zidane

D Rudi Völler

What happened to Alfredo Di Stefano in 1963 whilst on tour with Real Madrid in Venezuela?

444

A He was mobbed by angry fans following Real Madrid's victory over the Venezuelan national team

B He disappeared with a Venezuelan girl and got married

C He became embroiled in an argument in a bar in Caracus, narrowly escaping intact when it descended into a shoot-out

D He was kidnapped

What did Eusébio do while a fierce argument raged between Sporting Lisbon and Benfica about which of the teams had signed him?

445

A He hid in a fishing village

B He flew home to Mozambique and got married

C He taught football at a Portuguese school

D He signed for a Spanish club

Why was Aston Villa's first ever match a little unusual?

446

A One half was played as soccer, the other half as rugby

B It was played in Ireland

C It lasted just eighteen minutes

D It was played on the side of a 1:10 hill

447

What made both Dynamo Berlin and Dynamo Moscow somewhat unpopular?

A Their readiness to feign injury

B Their aggressive tactics on the pitch

C Their links with the secret police

D Their ability to buy up the best players thanks to government subsidies

448

What made a Blackburn Rovers v Burnley match in 1891 particularly difficult for Rovers' goalkeeper, Herby Arthur?

A His was playing with a broken arm

B He entire team walked off the field, leaving him to take on the opposition alone

C Blackburn's defenders had taken bribes to underperform

D Burnley chose to play with six players up front

449

How did football-crazy Canon A. Wellesley Orr frequently begin his church services?

A With a blow on a referee's whistle

B By heading a ball into the congregation

C With a short blast on a Klaxon horn

D By waving his favorite team's scarf and shouting 'Goooaaal!'

What was unusual about Czech football player Jan Skorkovsky's completion of the Prague City Marathon in 1990?

450

A He carried his team captain on his shoulders for the full 26 miles

B He kept a football in the air with his feet for the entire marathon, without it once touching the ground

C He continuously headed a football for the full distance without it once touching the ground

D He completed the marathon on a unicycle, balancing a football on his head

---

In 1927, Manchester United secured a Stockport County player in exchange for what?

451

A Chocolate

B Ice cream

C Butter

D Marmalade

What did the Italian government guarantee to the national squad if they secured victory against England upon their encounter in 1934?

452

A The Italian equivalent to a knighthood

B Tax exemption for life

C Protection from Mafia extortionists

D Exemption from military service

453

What happened shortly after Columbia were knocked out of the 1994 World Cup?

A All Columbian based members of the squad were dropped by their respective clubs

B Several members of the team were arrested for possession of drugs

C A number of the team attempted to claim asylum rather than return home

D One of the Columbian players was shot dead

454

What was so extraordinary about Wilf Minter's seven-goal rampage for St. Albans during their match against Dulwich Hamlet in 1922?

A His team lost the game

B He was the goalkeeper

C It was his debut match for the club

D He sustained an injury within ten minutes but continued to play

455

What did English players agree to do prior to kick-off against Germany in 1938?

A Wear lederhosen instead of shorts

B Substitute the National Anthem for 'Rule Britannia'

C Perform the Nazi salute

D Parade the Union Jack on the pitch during half-time

Why did Bristol City field a team in 1941 that comprised a spectator, a schoolteacher, a soldier, their opponents' trainer and five of their opponents' reserve players?

456

A A number of Bristol City's players fell out with the club manager and headed home just minutes before the match

B Several of their own players got lost on the way to the match

C The Bristol City team were struck down with food poisoning after a lunch stop

D Bristol City were in financial difficulty and couldn't afford to pay their players for the match

Why did the Indian national team withdraw from the 1950 World Cup, having achieved qualification for the first time?

457

A They couldn't afford transportation to the event

B Their request to play barefoot was turned down

C Several of their players refused to travel by air and there wasn't time to transport them any other way

D They didn't feel they stood a chance of beating any of the teams drawn in their group and wanted to avoid humiliation

458

Bon-Accord's record 36-0 defeat by Arbroath in 1885 could be considered a little unfair for what reason?

A Many of Bon-Accord's players were fishermen, who had just returned from an exhausting fishing trip

B Bon-Accord could only muster eight players in time for the game

C Bon-Accord's players were cricketers

D Bon-Accord's players hadn't played a match for more than six months

459

What was the Valley Party?

A The celebration resulting from Wales' World Cup qualification in 1958

B An annual social event held for linesmen and referees in the Wye Valley

C A political party established by Charlton Athletic fans to bring their club back to its traditional home

D Charlton's celebrations following their FA Cup win in 1947

460

What was the record-breaking sum for an English goalkeeper paid by Arsenal in 1990 to acquire David Seaman?

A £1m/$1.5m

B £2.5m/$3.75m

C £1.8m/$2.7m

D £1.3m/$1.95m

461

Which of these great 'Zs' was not a goalkeeper?

A Ricardo Zamora

B Ivan Zamorano

C Andoni Zubizaretta

D Dino Zoff

462

Prior to a change of rules in the early eighties, a goalkeeper's shirt had to be one of three colors. Which of the following was not one of the regulation colors?

A White

B Green

C Yellow

D Blue

463

In which year did Pat Jennings make his international debut as Northern Ireland's goalkeeper?

A 1962
B 1968
C 1964
D 1966

464

What were goalkeepers originally known as?

A Gate-keepers
B Postmen
C Goal-hangers
D Net-minders

465

What was so unforgettable about goalkeeper Marc de Clercs' debut for Aberdeen in 1980?

A He scored against the opposition from a clearance
B He conceded eighteen goals
C He was knocked unconscious by the first shot on goal
D He saved six penalties

Dave Beasant was the first goalkeeper to do what during an FA Cup Final at Wembley?

466

A Take a penalty

B Save a penalty

C Get sent off

D Captain his team

Walsall fielded a record number of goalkeepers during the 1972-73 season. How many in total played in league matches for the club?

467

A 7

B 11

C 5

D 9

When the great, pre-World War One goalkeeper, Leigh Richmond Roose was late for an away match what action did he take?

468

A He cycled and turned up in time for the second half

B He had his own bi-plane and flew there

C He took a hansom cab

D He hired a train to take him there at once

469

Which goalkeeper prompted the FA to change the 18-yard box rules when he used to carry the ball to the other end of the field?

A Ted Ditchburn

B Lev Yashin

C Leigh Richmond Roose

D Jack Kelsey

470

Which goalkeeper's hands were described as 'Lurgan Shovels'?

A Joe Corrigan

B Ray Clemence

C Shay Given

D Pat Jennings

471

Why was goalkeeper Frank Haffey's only international appearance for Scotland disastrous?

A He set a new world record for the number of corner kicks conceded in a game

B He let in nine goals

C He dived into goalpost and knocked himself out

D He punched the referee instead of the ball

In which year were the German national team forced to split, becoming East Germany and West Germany?

472

A 1945
B 1946
C 1948
D 1947

Gerd Müller holds which German international record?

473

A Most bookings at international levels
B Most international appearances
C Highest number of goals during a single German international match
D Most international goals for his country

How many caps and how many goals did Jürgen Klinsmann rack up during his West German international career?

474

A 98 caps, 42 goals
B 98 caps, 47 goals
C 108 caps, 47 goals
D 108 caps, 42 goals

475

West Germany's Sepp Maier played in which position?

A Forward

B Midfield

C Defense

D Goal

476

In which city did Germany lift the World Cup for the first time in their footballing history?

A Geneva

B Stockholm

C Bern

D Bonn

477

Who was 'Der Bomber'?

A Uwe Seeler

B Gerd Müller

C Rudi Völler

D Karl-Heinz Rummenigge

Italy's third World Cup title was achieved under whose management?

478

A Vittorio Pozzo

B Vincenzo Pozzo

C Enzo Ferrari

D Enzo Bearzot

Following their quarter-final draw against Spain in the 1934 World Cup, how long did Italy have to wait for the rematch that saw them through to the semi-finals?

479

A A month

B A week

C Until the next day

D Two weeks

Which country were the source of Italian embarrassment during the 1966 World Cup finals?

480

A Vietnam

B Qatar

C North Korea

D South Korea

481

When Dino Zoff lifted the World Cup in 1982 he also entered the record books for what?

A Being the oldest World Cup-winning goalkeeper

B Being the first goalkeeper to captain a World Cup-winning team

C Being the first European goalkeeper to captain a World Cup-winning team

D Being the first goalkeeper to maintain a clean sheet for the duration of a World Cup finals tournament

482

Paulo Rossi and Salvatore Schillachi have both won which award?

A FIFA World Player of the Year

B FIFA Fair Play Award

C A Soulier d'Or (Golden Boot for top League goalscorer in Europe)

D A World Cup Golden Boot

Traditionally, what color were professional, laced leather footballs?

483

A Brown

B White

C Black

D Grey

When was a football made from synthetic material first used in a World Cup Final?

484

A 1974

B 1978

C 1986

D 1990

What was the color of the ball used for the 1966 World Cup Final?

485

A White

B Orange

C Brown

D Grey

486

The Laws of the Game state what as being the permissible circumference of a football?

- **A** 24-25 inches
- **B** 25-26 inches
- **C** 26-27 inches
- **D** 27-28 inches

487

And what is the permitted weight of a ball?

- **A** 12-14 oz
- **B** 18-20 oz
- **C** 16-18 oz
- **D** 14-16 oz

488

For what reason were white footballs introduced to the game?

- **A** The color was more suitable for matches held at night
- **B** White balls were more visible to television spectators
- **C** To differentiate synthetic balls from leather balls
- **D** The new synthetic materials were originally only available in white

– Load of Balls –

489

Under what circumstances is it permissible for an orange football to be used during a professional match?

- **A** At night
- **B** When it's snowing
- **C** For a World Cup final
- **D** If one of the competing teams is playing in a white strip

490

Football leagues for the partially-sighted place what inside the match ball to make it 'audible'?

- **A** Marbles
- **B** Small bells
- **C** Ball bearings
- **D** Nut kernels

491

Should a ball burst whilst in play in a penalty area, how should the referee restart the match?

- **A** With a goal kick from the penalty area in which the ball burst
- **B** With a drop ball from the nearest point on the edge of the goal area
- **C** With a drop ball from the center circle
- **D** With a throw on, taken by a player representing the last team to touch the ball

492 What is the Golden Boot?

- **A** The decisive goal-scoring shot during extra time
- **B** The award given to the top scorer in the World Cup Finals or European league
- **C** The award presented to the European Footballer of the Year
- **D** The award presented to World Footballer of the Year

493 What is the conclusive goal during extra time known as?

- **A** The Golden Goal
- **B** The Golden Ball
- **C** The Golden Goose
- **D** The Golden Shot

494 What term is applied to a player barred from a Cup competition because he has already played in the same competition with a different team?

- **A** Cup-bound
- **B** Cup-held
- **C** Cup-tied
- **D** Cup-blocked

Who beat Brazil to win the 1995 FIFA Under-17 World
Championship Final?

A Saudi Arabia

B Nigeria

C Spain

D Ghana

OTHER TITLES

There are many other exciting quiz
and puzzle books in the IntelliQuest range,
and your QUIZMO electronic unit
knows the answers to them all!

You can order from your local
IntelliQuest stockist or on-line bookseller.

For a full listing of current titles
(and ISBN numbers) see:

www.thelagoongroup.com/intelliquest

LAGOON
BOOKS